English Class on Mars

Taylor Sapp

Alphabet Publishing

Contents

Before You Read

1. What do you know about Mars? Would you like to visit there someday?

2. Do you think people will live on other planets someday?

3. Will we ever coexist with aliens?

4. What comes to mind when you think of the following types of students?

- Teacher's pet

- Troublemaker

- Class clown

- Jock

English Class on Mars

Professor Smith stood outside the classroom, looking in through the window of the door nervously. The classroom was nearly full, but almost none of the students were human. Teaching aliens was not part of Smith's experience, so he was nervous. Looking at the attendance list, Smith saw four clearly human names. Searching the room with his eyes, he found the humans, in colors ranging from black to brown to white. Their parents were humans working on the Mars Space Station. The kids had never been to Earth and, in some ways, they were as foreign as the aliens.

The rest of the class were native Martians. Their colors were red, green, purple, blue, or orange. There was nearly one student to represent each color of the rainbow! The collection of mouths, eyes, arms, tentacles, and other features, was also alien.

Smith had never been in space before. He had never met aliens. He knew that Earthlings had space stations and even cities on other planets. He'd seen aliens on the news and in movies, but never up close. He'd never imagined he would have to interact with them.

Professor Smith had taught English to incoming foreigners at the University of Branford for 20 years. He had a Masters in Teaching English and a PhD in American culture and he loved preparing new students at his university, guaranteeing they would succeed. Of course, then alien life was discovered. Eventually, Earthlings came to live on other planets and aliens came to Earth. It was only a matter of time before universities started offering classes on Earth languages and life so that aliens could feel at home on the blue planet. Professor Smith had taken the job on Mars—the pay was three times as high as on Earth and he was given a beautiful apartment in the space station, among other perks.

But he couldn't help regretting his decision as he walked into the classroom. Gazing at all of the strange creatures, he felt so nervous and a bit shocked, frankly. How could he teach something without visible eyes or three mouths or tentacles instead of arms?

Professor Smith stood at the desk in front, took a deep breath and began to speak.

"Good morning" he began slowly, "My name is Dr. Smith and I will be teaching you about the English language, as well as American Earth culture. I am new to Mars so I hope you will be easy with me as I get used to some new aspects about your planet's way of life." The difference in gravity had given him a headache and stomachache he was still recovering from.

"Loser!" One of the Earth males looked angrily at the teacher, while the other human male laughed, before returning to staring at their smart devices.

Smith decided to ignore the attitude and look for the teacher's pet to win over. He went immediately to the two human girls, one black, one likely Asian. On the attendance list, their names were written as Monica and Suki.

"Ladies, you were born on Mars, so you could probably educate us all on this planet."

The two girls looked at each other and laughed. They said something in Martian that he couldn't understand. The tone suggested it was a rude insult.

The humans all laughed together, and Professor Smith could only stare. He'd never faced this kind of attitude. He was at a loss.

Suddenly, a loud shriek silenced the room.

"Hey!" Sixco, a green-skinned petite girl with three eyes, spoke with a high-pitched voice. "My parents paid a lot to send me here! They wouldn't bring this brainy teacher to teach us if he didn't know what he was talking about!" She turned to Smith, "I would like to welcome you to our class and planet."

Another purple alien, whose name tag displayed only some symbols that Smith couldn't pronounce, spoke with a single open mouth, "Just ignore them and go ahead, please."

Shocked, Smith glanced around the room to see the faces of the rainbow-colored aliens looking at him quietly and patiently, while the humans Connor and Preston stared at their phones and Suki and Monica worked on their lip gloss and makeup.

"Please teacher, continue." An orange alien with eight eyes spoke through a small, circular mouth. He was holding his e-notebook, and prepared to take notes.

And so Professor Smith started the lesson he'd prepared.

· · · ● · ● · ● · ·

At the end of his first day, he sat in the teacher's room. Another professor, an alien, approached him.

Red (both in color and name, for he said his real name was unpronounceable by humans) was a red stone-covered humanoid with a loud but gentle voice. He introduced himself as the math professor.

"I think you are teaching my son."

He remembered the diligent student taking notes, the one with the eight eyes, who looked a lot like Red.

"He seems like a good kid."

Rod nodded, his eight eyes moving in all directions. "If you need any help, ask me or my son. You should learn quickly, teacher. Humans will give you nothing but trouble."

"Well, thank heavens for the Martians then, at least."

He never thought he would have said that.

Glossary

alien: a creature from another planet

brainy: smart

diligent: hard-working

Earthlings: people from Earth

gravity: the force that makes things stay on a planet

high-pitched: high in musical tone, like a flute or whistle

humanoid: looking like a human being

loser: (*here*) an insult, a person you don't respect

makeup: products people put on their face to make them look more attractive

perks: benefits of a job besides the salary

petite: short and small, usually used to describe women

shriek: a loud scream, like a hawk

silenced: caused people to stop making noise

tentacles: arm-like limbs. Octopuses and squid have tentacles

unpronounceable: containing sounds that the speaker cannot make

After You Read

1. What is unusual about Professor Smith's classroom?

2. Why is he nervous?

3. Why does he start by talking to the human girl? Does he get what he wants from her?

4. Which student helps him? Why is he surprised by that?

5. Who is Red? What advice does he give Professor Smith?

6. What do you think will happen at the next class?

7. What moral could you give this story?

8. Do you think we will ever co-exist with aliens? What kinds of problems will we face?

Writing

Write what happens next.

- How does Professor Smith's second day of class go?

- How do the students react to him the next day?

- Do the humans change their attitude?

- What other challenges does he face?

More Readers

Baby Shopping
Changes
Empathy
English Class on Mars
Ghost in My Room
Magic Employment Agency
Rebirth
Attack of the Sleep Demon
The AI Therapist
Thought Police
Time Travel Research: Genghis Khan
Virtual Unreality

AlphabetPublish.com/Book-Category/
Graded-Reader

Printed in the USA
CPSIA information can be obtained
at www.ICGtesting.com
JSHW011140071024
70794JS00006B/128